Ros Bayley
Beanbag Raps

ACKNOWLEDGEMENTS

Written by: Ros Bayley
(in association with Lynn Broadbent)

Illustrated by: Peter Scott

Produced by: Lynda Lawrence.

Published by: Lawrence Educational
17 Redruth Road, Walsall,
West Midlands, WS5 3EJ

©   Lawrence Educational 2005.

ISBN: 1-903670-43-8

Introduction

We all need a sense of steady beat when performing any task involving sophisticated movement, i.e. when walking, dancing, writing, cutting with scissors, hammering in a nail or drawing. In fact, it is so essential that if someone lacks beat awareness, he or she usually have difficulty with both gross and fine motor skills.

Recent studies have even shown a correlation of beat competency to school achievement that exceeds that of either social class or mother's education, these latter two being the usual predictors of school success. By helping children to develop beat competency we can improve their chances of success.

There are a wide range of ways in which we can help children to develop beat competency, but the more that young children have opportunities to engage in singing, dancing and rapping and play with instruments, jingles and rhymes, the better they will get.

The raps in this book can all be chanted to a steady beat, and as the children learn them they will also be developing listening and language skills. The beanbag raps are particularly good for teaching 'action' words and positional language.

Ros Bayley

Introductory Rap

*(This rap can be used to introduce
any of the other raps)*

If you're ready shout yes.

YES!

If you're steady shout yes.

YES!

If you're ready and steady
shout yes, yes, yes.

YES, YES, YES!

Rap 1

Put your beanbag up high
Put your beanbag down low
Put your beanbag up high
Put your beanbag down low
Front and back
High and low
Front and back
High and low
Front and back
High and low
Now lift it up
And let it go!

At the end of the rap the children pick up the
beanbag and begin again.

Rap 2

Round your head
Under your leg
Touch your nose
Then your toes
Round your head
Under your leg
Nose and toes
That's how it goes!

Repeat as many times as you like.

Rap 3

Stand up straight
With your beanbag in your hand
Then drop it on the floor
And watch it land
Walk all around it
One two, three
Then stand as still
As still can be!

Rap 4

Shake your beanbag
Shake your beanbag
Shake it up and down
Now put it on your head
And wear it like a crown
Take one step forward
Stand up tall
Do not let your beanbag fall!

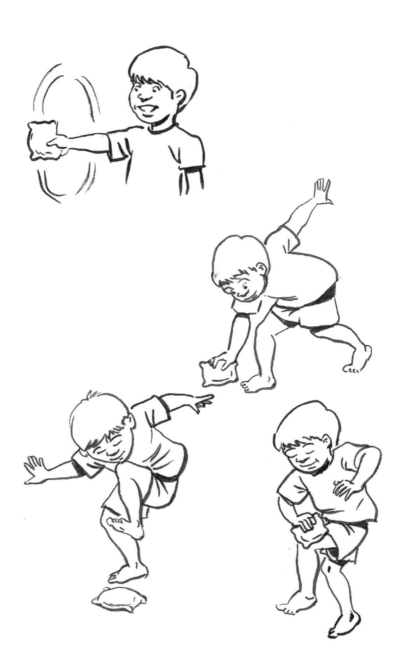

Rap 5

Make a circle with your beanbag

Move it round and round

Now bend right down

And touch the ground

Stamp on your beanbag

One, two, three

Then pick it up again

And tap it on your knee

One, two, three

One, two, three

One, two, three

Tap it on your knee!

Rap 6

Throw your beanbag
High in the air
Watch it land
Leave it there
Creep right up to it
Hold it in your hand
Now go and put it down
Where you'd like to stand.

Children then repeat the rap from their new space.

Rap 7

Tap your beanbag on your toes

Now up your leg

Keep on going

'Till it touches your head

Now back down again

'Till you reach your toes

Put your beanbag in your other hand

Ready to go!

The rap is then repeated on the other side of the body.

Rap 8

For all of the following raps the children will need two beanbags.

One beanbag on your shoulder

One beanbag on your knee

Swap them over, swap them over

Swap them over like me.

One beanbag on your head

One beanbag on your ear

Hold your beanbags out far

Then hold them near

One beanbag on your nose

One beanbag on your ear

Hold your beanbags out in front

Now hold them to the rear.

Rap 9

For this rap the children stand in a circle with a beanbag in each hand.

Hold both beanbags out

Stamp to the beat

Bring your beanbags down

To touch your feet

Now lift them up again

And wind them round

Then put them all together

In one big mound.

The children then select a different beanbag and begin the rap again.

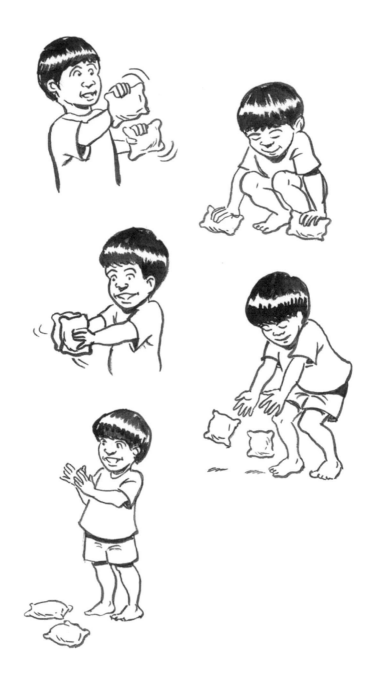

Rap 10

Out, up, wind them round

Tap your beanbags on the ground

Front, back, slap, slap *(children slap their beanbags together)*

Beanbags down *(children put beanbags on the floor)*

Clap, clap *(clap hands together)*

Pick beanbags up again and repeat the rhyme.
It can be repeated as many times as you like.

Rap 11

Wind the bobbin round *(using the beanbags)*
As you hear this sound
Keep on going
'Till you reach the ground
Put one beanbag high
Put one beanbag low
Swap them over
Now go, go, go!

Rap 12

Put your beanbags out
Put your beanbags in
Put your beanbags out
Tap them on your chin
Put your beanbags high
Put your beanbags low
Cross your arms over
Let your beanbags go!

Children then pick their beanbags up and begin again.

Rap 13

For this rap the children sit with their legs crossed and a beanbag in each hand.

Knees *(tap beanbags on knees)*
Together *(tap beanbags together)*
Knees
Together
Nose *(tap beanbags on nose)*
Nose
Nose
Knees
Together
Knees
Together
Toes *(tap beanbags on toes)*
Toes
Toes

Repeat as many times as you like.

Rap 14

Knees
Together
Knees
Together
Wind your beanbags round
Knees
Together
Knees
Together
Ground *(tap beanbags on the ground)*
Ground
Ground!

Repeat as many times as you like, and once the children have got the hang of it, join raps 13 and 14 together.

Rap 15

For this rap each child will need a set of number cards. You can also use picture cards or word cards.

Tap your beanbags

Tap your beanbags

Tap them on your knees

Shake your beanbags

Shake your beanbags

Hard as can be

Squeeze your beanbags

Squeeze your beanbags

Squeeze them really hard

Then put your beanbags down

On the number _ card.

We hope you have enjoyed our 'Beanbag Raps'.

Other books in the same series are:

Ros Bayley's **Animal Raps**   ISBN: 1-903670-38-1

Ros Bayley's **Action Raps**   ISBN: 1-903670-42-X

Additional rhymes and further guidance on developing children's beat competency can be found in our '**Helping Young Children With Steady Beat**' resource pack.

Included with this pack is a small cuddly toy called BEAT BABY, who can be used at the beginning and end of sessions to help focus the children and to bring emotional engagement to the whole process.

ISBN: 1-903670-26-4

For further details of these and our many other publications, visit our website:

www.educationalpublications.com